Umar Farooq

(May Allah be pleased with him)

The Second Caliph of Islam

Sr. Nafees Khan
Vinni Rahman

GOODWORD

The Prophet Muhammad(Pbuh) gave Umar(ra) the title of "Al Farooq", which means, 'The one who distinguishes between right and wrong.' Once the Prophet said, "Allah has placed truth upon Umar's tongue and heart." He also said, "The truth after me is with Umar, wherever he may be."

These were the qualities which made Umar Farooq(ra) an extraordinary person. In the history of the world, he holds a unique position among the greatest of the kings, statesmen and administrators. Unlike them he was not guided by worldly ambition, but by his faith in Allah, His messenger and His book—the Quran. He became the head of the largest state in the world, but he himself lived the life of a common man, simple in his habits and austere in his living. Even the poorest person could reach him directly and he was concerned about all his citizens, whether they were Muslims or non-Muslims.

Umar(ra) was born in Makkah around 582 C.E. Both his father Khattab and his mother, Khantamah, were prominent members of the 'Adi, a branch of the Quraish, a clan from which judges and ambassadors were chosen. Whenever the Quraish had any disputes amongst themselves or with others, they were chosen as arbitrators. They were held in great respect as they could speak eloquently and possessed tact and judgment.

As a young boy, like those of his age, Umar(ra) also had to graze camels, goats and sheep, but unlike other children of Makkah, he learned to read and write. As a matter of fact, there were only sixteen other people in the whole of Makkah who could do so. This was surely a great achievement.

Umar(ra) grew up to be tall, with a very strong physique and an impressive personality. He was a champion wrestler and swordsman and was so accomplished as a rider that he could ride the wildest of horses with ease.

Umar(ra), sincere and straightforward, had strong convictions. He was extremely intelligent. He was always ready to help the weak. An amazing quality which Umar(ra) had was that he was always eager to learn from everyone. He was free from all kind of prejudices. He was interested in knowing his mistakes and to correct them. He was always very grateful to those who pointed out his faults and disliked those who tried to flatter him.

He displayed all the ancestral qualities including the art of public speaking and knowledge of genealogy. He had no difficulty in handling the responsibilities of an ambassador or in acting as an arbitrator for the Quraish.

As a rich successful merchant, he traveled to many foreign lands such as Iraq, Syria, Persia and Yemen and met all kinds of people including Arabian and Persian princes. This experience broadened his insight into the needs and problems and the nature of people.

The Prophet Muhammad(Pbuh) received his first revelation in 610 C.E. Later on when he started preaching about Islam the Quraish got angry and upset. They started to torture the Muslims, and eventually after some years when it became unbearable Muslims chose to leave Makkah. Umar(ra) was about twenty-seven years of age at that time and, whenever someone accepted Islam, he would become furious. He believed that this new faith was sacrilege against their various gods. Being a young man with strong convictions, he took it upon himself to stop the spread of this new religion in every possible way.

One day in 616 C.E., Umar(ra) set out, sword in hand, to kill the Prophet. On the way, a friend of his informed him that his own sister, Fatima had accepted Islam. Umar(ra) couldn't believe it, and to know the truth he went straight to her house. Fatima was reading the twentieth *Surah, Ta Ha* of the Quran and he heard the recitation. Fatima quickly hid it when she realized that Umar(ra) was there. After some exchange of words, Umar(ra) started beating his brother-in-law, Sa'eed. When Fatima tried to intervene she too was struck, which caused her to bleed. Fatima declared, "Umar, you can do what you like, but you cannot turn us away from Islam!" Umar(ra) loved his sister dearly and was moved at

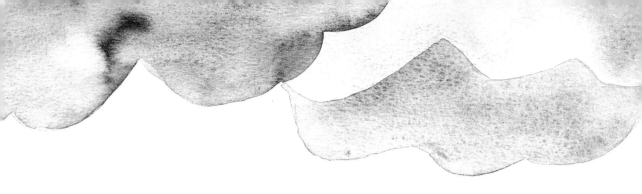

the sight of her blood and by her determination to follow her new faith. Overwhelmed with regret and guilt, he asked his sister to show him what she was reading. She handed him over the *Surah Ta Ha,* and he started reading it.

When he reached verse 14, **'I am Allah. There is no deity save Me; so worship Me alone, and say your prayers in My remembrance',** he felt as if these verses were addressed to him in person and Allah was talking to him. He immediately decided not to lose any more time in following the truth. He turned to his sister and brother-in-law and said, "I came to you as an enemy of Islam; I go from you as a friend of Islam. I buckled on this sword to slay the Prophet of Islam; I now go to him to offer my allegiance." Fatima and Sa'eed called out "Allahu Akbar!" (God is great!) He went to the Prophet and professed his faith in Islam. Soon everyone in Makkah came to know that Umar(ra) was no longer a bitter enemy of Islam but a staunch follower. He was the fortieth person to become a Muslim.

The conversion of Umar(ra) to Islam was in response to the prayer which the Prophet Muhammad(Pbuh) had made in the Kabah, "O Lord, make Islam strong with the conversion of either of the two men, Amr bin Hisham or Umar bin Al Khattab!"

Until now the Muslims had kept their faith private and prayed in secret. Umar(ra) asked, " O Messenger of Allah, are we not on the truth?" The Prophet answered, "Yes, we are indeed on the truth!" Umar(ra) continued, "Then why do we pray in hiding? Isn't it the time for us to declare our faith openly?" Umar(ra) persisted with his request until the Prophet agreed. Eventually, the Prophet Muhammad(Pbuh) led the prayers publicly for the first time in the Kabah.

By 622 C.E., the persecution of the Muslims had reached its peak, and they started migrating quietly in batches with the Prophet's permission. Umar(ra) left for Madinah accompanied by twenty others after announcing his intentions openly, but nobody among Quraish had the courage to stop him.

Upon his arrival in Madinah, the Prophet Muhammad(Pbuh) established a unique and strong 'brotherhood' to help settle the *'Muhajirs'* (migrants) with the *'Ansars'* (the people of Madinah). Utban bin Malik, who was a chieftain, was chosen as Umar's(ra) brother-in-faith.

With the growth in the numbers of Muslims, the Prophet wanted to decide upon a way of calling the faithful to prayers. He and some *Sahaba* (Companions) started considering the use of some kind of musical instrument similar to that of the Jews and the Christians, but at that point, Umar(ra) related a dream he had had, and suggested, "Why not appoint a man for this purpose?" The Prophet then sent for Bilal and asked him to perform the *'adhaan'* (the call to prayers). Therefore, the credit goes to Umar(ra) for the establishment of the *'adhaan'*, which is echoed in every masjid around the globe to this day. He was the one who also inserted

the line 'Prayer is better than sleep' in the *adhaan* for morning prayers.

Subsequently, it was he who instituted the prayers of *Tarawih* in congregation in the masjid in the month of *Ramadan*. It was he who established the *Hijri* calendar, which began in the year of *hijrat* (migration).

From the time of migration till the death of the Prophet, Umar(ra) was actively involved in all the important events. The Prophet consulted with Abu Bakr and Umar(ra) in all matters of significance. The Prophet Muhammad(Pbuh) once said, "If you two agreed upon any matter, I would not oppose you."

As Umar(ra) was generous, he was always eager to contribute financially to the cause of Islam and gave away most of his wealth for it. He stood by the side of the Prophet in all his trials

and tribulations. His love for the Prophet knew no bounds. In 625 C.E, Hafsah, the widowed daughter of Umar(ra) was married to the Prophet Muhammad(Pbuh), which further brought them closer.

When the Prophet Muhammad(Pbuh) passed away in 632 C.E. after a brief illness, everyone was grief stricken. Umar(ra) was beside himself with shock. He could not imagine how Islam and Muslims would cope without him. Abu Bakr(ra), trying to calm the people said, "O people, those of you who worshipped Muhammad know that he is dead like any other mortal. But those who worship Allah know that He is alive and will live forever." But Umar(ra) was still inconsolable and then, Abu Bakr(ra) quoted the following verses of the Quran. "Muhammad is only a messenger. Messengers have passed away before him. If he should die, or be killed, will you turn back on your heels? Those who turn on their heels do not harm the Lord in the least. Allah will reward the grateful. No soul should die except with Allah's permission and at an appointed time." (3:144,145)

Later, recalling this day, Umar(ra) narrated, "By God, I heard Abu Bakr(ra) recite these verses. I was so dumbfounded that my legs would not bear me, and I fell to the ground, knowing that the Holy Prophet was indeed dead."

The *Ansars* had gathered at a meeting place and were arguing as to who should be the leader, after Prophet's death. When Abu Bakr(ra), Umar(ra) and Abu Ubaidah arrived there, they found the Muslim community was on the verge of splitting. Thinking quickly, Umar(ra), took the initiative and declared his support for Abu Bakr(ra) by pointing out the various hints given by the Prophet Muhammad(Pbuh) on this subject.

Abu Bakr(ra) was a Caliph for only a short time and Umar(ra) was one of his chief advisors. It was Umar(ra) who had convinced Abu Bakr(ra) to have the Quran compiled in the form of a book after the battle of Yamama.

Just before his death in 634 C.E., after consulting the senior *Sahaba*, Abu Bakr(ra) chose Umar(ra) as his successor by declaring, "My brothers in faith, I have not appointed any of my own relatives as your Caliph, but Umar(ra). Do you accept this decision? " The people responded, "We listen and we obey!" Umar(ra) accepted the position reluctantly.

Following Abu Bakr's(ra) death, Umar(ra) addressed the people gathered in Masjid un Nabi.

"…..In the performance of my duties, I will seek guidance from the Quran and will follow the examples set by Prophet(Pbuh) and Abu Bakr(ra). In this task I seek your help. If I follow the right path, follow me. If I stray from the right path, correct me so that we are not led astray…." Umar(ra) went on to say, "…Read the Quran. Acquire knowledge through it and act upon it. Thus you will become the followers of the Quran. Keep holding yourself to account before you are held to account, for self-examination will render your accounting easy. And weigh yourselves before you are weighed; and prepare yourselves for the great trial when you are produced before Allah Most High. On that day, nothing of your hidden matters will remain covered."

After two visitors to Madinah had referred to Umar(ra) as " Ameer ul Mu'mineen" (Leader of the Muslims), he decided to use this title, and it was later used by all the Caliphs.

In 635 C.E the Muslim army left Madinah for Iraq under the command of Saad bin Abi Waqqas to face the Persians and take back what they had conquered. Umar(ra) determined the route and the places where the army would stop. He even studied the maps of the area in making these decisions, drawing upon his experience of previous journeys. He divided the troops into regiments, chose the commanders and gave instructions after carefully considering every detail. In short, he made all the essential decisions. Then Umar(ra) asked Saad bin Abi Waqqas to offer peace to the Persians and use diplomacy to avoid a battle. Fourteen Muslim chiefs of different tribes were sent as envoys. But the peace initiative failed and the battle began in 636 CE. It was a long battle in which the Persians used elephants as 'tanks'. Muslims were victorious in the end, even though their army was much smaller. Rustam, the legendary Persian commander, was also killed during this battle.

Some time later, after taking the White Palace on the banks of the River Tigris in Madain from the Persians, Saad sent enormous

treasure to Madinah. Upon seeing the glittering pile in the Masjid un Nabi, Umar's(ra) eyes swelled up with tears.

One of the men present commented, "There is nothing to cry about." Umar(ra) responded, "I am crying because riches give rise to hostility and mutual hatred. A nation which has these evils loses its respect!" Umar(ra) praised the honesty of the Muslim soldiers who had not kept back anything unlawfully. "O Ameer ul Mu'mineen, when you yourself set such a high example of honesty, why should your people not be honest?" said Ali(ra).

When Jerusalem was under siege by the Muslim generals in 637 C.E., and the mighty Byzantine army was defeated, the Christians decided to give in. They had heard about the just and tolerant ways of the Muslims in dealing with the people of the conquered places. However, they insisted that the Caliph himself must come and sign the peace treaty, as they wanted to make sure that they would be treated well. Therefore, a letter was sent to the Caliph explaining their condition and requesting him to come to Palestine.

On receiving this letter, Umar Farooq(ra) left Madinah for Jerusalem with only one servant and one camel. As he left the city, he said to his servant, "We are two and the mount is one. If I ride and you go on foot, I shall be doing you an injustice. And if we both ride, that will be an injustice to the camel. So we better take it in turns to ride." So they alternately rode and went on foot, then they would both go on foot for some time to give the camel some respite. They went on in this way until they were approaching Jerusalem, when, by chance, it was the servant's turn to ride. The servant declined to sit on the camel's back so that the Caliph might be on the mount while entering the city. But Umar Farooq(ra) did not agree to this. And so the Caliph reached the

16

gates of Jerusalem with the servant on the camel's back and himself on foot wearing rough clothes. The inhabitants gaped at the sight which they could not even have imagined. Witnessing this sight, the priests opened the gates and directly made peace with Umar Farooq(ra).

Umar(ra) signed the following agreement; an example of a more just and considerate treaty is difficult to be found in history:

"This is the protection that the servant of Allah, Umar bin Al Khattab, Ameer ul Mu'mineen, has offered to all the people of Jerusalem. The protection is for their lives and properties, their churches and their crosses, their sick and healthy. Their churches

shall not be used as homes nor shall they be destroyed. There should be no compulsion on them in the matter of religion. If anyone wishes to leave, they can leave freely and take their belongings." After the completion of the peace treaty, Caliph Umar(ra) made a short speech in which he said: 'O people of Palestine, what is for us is for you. What is not for us is not for you either."

During this visit he went with the Patriarch to visit various holy places. One day when Umar(ra) was sitting in the courtyard of the Church of Qiama in Jerusalem, the time came for the afternoon prayer. Umar(ra) then turned to the Patriarch and asked where he should say his prayers. The priest replied that he could pray right where he was seated. Umar(ra), however, said, "No, it is not proper for Umar to pray inside the Church, because any Muslim who comes here afterwards, will maintain that since Umar(ra) has said his prayers here, a masjid should be built on that very spot.' Umar(ra), therefore, moved a stone's throw away, and said his prayers. Muslims did come to the city later on and, as he had foreseen, built their masjid at the exact point where he had said his prayers. This masjid exists to this day – a short, but discreet distance away from the Church. This discretion shown by Umar(ra) is all the more remarkable for his having been the ruler of Palestine at that time and, therefore, in a position to do anything he wished. A man with less foresight would have regarded praying inside the Church as a harmless event. But Umar(ra) could foresee that this act could in future become a cause of dispute and unnecessary trouble.

During Umar's(ra) Caliphate, Egypt, Iraq, Palestine, Persia and Syria, a total area of 2,251,030 square miles, came under Islamic rule. The conquered territories were dealt with tolerance. Jews and Christians who had been persecuted under the Byzantines appreciated this. Their customs and rules were taken into account while making laws, something hitherto unheard of.

During his Caliphate many new cities were founded like Kufa, Basra and Fustat. These cities were properly planned, and many masajid, orphanages, market places, public utilities and administrative buildings were constructed. He was against the construction of palatial buildings.

Umar(ra) stood for simplicity and austerity. Much public work was done all over the empire. Canals were dug to irrigate fields and roads and bridges were constructed for public use. Many shelters, guest houses, wells and eating places were built on the roadsides for the public.

Prison houses and military cantonments were made along with stables for the cavalry at various strategic points.

Caliph Umar(ra) established a new administrative structure.

Departments of the army, police, education, judiciary, public works and public treasury were formed. He was the first ruler in the history of the world to separate judiciary from the executive. The *Qadis* (Judges) were chosen for their integrity and learning in Islamic law. Nowhere had anything like this ever been done before.

Umar(ra) created laws which showed complete human consideration, such as no army personnel being sent away from their families for more than four months at a time.

He selected and appointed honest and capable men to high positions with the approval and consent of the *Sahaba*. Umar(ra) would also take a promise from them to lead a simple life and told

them, "Remember, I have not appointed you as commanders and tyrants over the people. I have sent you as leaders, so that people may follow your example. Do not behave as if you are superior to them, for that would amount to cruelty." The appointed governors and officers were given powers and obligations in the presence of others in order to keep the public informed of their rights. They were expected to keep their doors open without a security guard.

A written list of an officer's possessions was kept as a record. If any unusual financial increase was reported, the officers would be summoned to give explanations. Any invalid increase would be confiscated and sent to *Bait ul Mal* (public treasury). At the time of *Hajj* all the officers were required to come to Makkah. People from all over the Islamic world had a chance to voice their grievances against any officer and their concerns were taken care of immediately.

Umar(ra) would make enquiries about governors from envoys from the lands he ruled over. Was he a ruler who cared about his subjects, did he visit slaves and walk in funeral processions? Was he accessible to his people and sympathetic towards those who came to his door? If the answers were that he heard cases sympathetically and looked after slaves well, Umar(ra) would permit his rule to continue, but otherwise he would promptly appoint another governor to relieve him of his post.

He did not just give orders but saw to it that they were carried out. Whatever Umar(ra) expected from the governors he himself did, in fact, he did much more than he asked them to do. Umar(ra) not only set an example but also applied stricter rules to himself. His officers were paid a high salary, while what he drew was at poverty level.

Umar(ra) had the highest regard for human equality and human respect. This, in effect, removed all kinds of differences between men. Umar(ra) even treated Muslims and non-Muslims equally. He was completely just in his dealings as a ruler and also as a person. The following event illustrates this.

Amr ibn al-As was the governor of Egypt during his Caliphate. One day the governor organized a horse race in which his own son, Muhammad ibn Amr ibn al-As, also took part. But in the race, the horse of the governor's son was beaten by the horse of a Copt, a non-Muslim. The Copt expressed his joy and this hurt the governor's son. He lashed the Copt with his whip, saying, "Take that! I am the son of a nobleman!"

The Copt came from Egypt to Madinah, the capital, and complained to Umar(ra) that the governor's son had whipped him. Umar(ra) asked him to stay in Madinah and, after enquiring into the details and discovering the truth, he immediately sent a special messenger to bring Amr ibn aI-As and his son without delay to Madinah. When they arrived, they were both brought before the Caliph. Then the latter sent for the young Copt and asked him if this was the man who had beaten him. When the Copt replied in the affirmative, the Caliph handed him a whip and asked him to flog this 'son of a nobleman.' The Copt did so, and went on flogging him till he felt that justice had been done. Then the Caliph asked him also to flog Amr ibn aI-As, the father of the young wrongdoer, as it had been his high status – as Umar(ra) explained – which had encouraged the son to take his whip to him. But then the Copt said, "No, I have whipped the person who whipped me, and I wish no more than that."

Umar(ra) said to the Copt: 'By God! If you had beaten him (the governor) we would not have intervened, until you yourself had stopped beating him. Then Umar(ra) turned to Amr ibn aI-As and said: 'O Amr, since when have you enslaved people who were born free?

Many times when foreign envoys or messengers came to Madinah, they found him resting under a palm tree or in the masjid amongst the people, and it was difficult to distinguish which man was the Caliph.

24

Caliph Umar
Farooq(ra), ruled over
a large part of Asia and
Africa, but continued to wear
very ordinary clothes which often
had patches. He would carry water
bags over his shoulders. He would sleep
on the ground with a stone as a pillow. He
ate simple food and lived in an ordinary
house.

Some people from Iraq once came to see Umar(ra). When it
was time for food, he brought them a big bowl containing
whole wheat bread and olive oil, and asked them to eat. They
started eating very slowly, and a little at a time. "I can see
what you are doing, people of Iraq," Umar(ra) said to them.

"You know, if I wanted, I could have lavish and delicious food such as you have. But we leave over our portion of the world so that we may partake of it in the Hereafter. Have you not heard what Allah said about a certain group of people? 'You wasted away your precious things in your earthly life.'"

Once Ahnaf ibn Qays came to see him in Madinah. He found him desperately running around. When Ahnaf asked Umar(ra) what was the matter, he replied that a camel belonging to *Bait al-Mal* (public treasury) had gone astray and that he was looking for it. Ahnaf said, "You are the leader of the believers *(Amirul-Muminin)*. Why are you taking all this trouble? *You* should have asked a servant to do this for you." Caliph Umar(ra) replied, "Who is a greater servant than I am?"

Considering oneself a common man, while in actuality being the ruler of an empire, gave a practical example of the humility expected of a ruler who obeyed the Islamic code of ethics.

Caliph Umar(ra) often spent nights going around the city to see whether anyone needed help. He used to visit the old and sick and even did their housework. He also visited the families of the soldiers to ensure that they were taken care of.

One night as usual, during the year of the famine (640 C.E) Umar(ra) went on his rounds to make sure no one went to sleep hungry. He came to a dwelling where he saw a woman cooking something and a couple of children sitting nearby and crying. Umar(ra) went up to her to inquire what the matter was. He was told that they had not had any food and to console the children she was pretending to cook. "I am pretending to cook food but it is just water and stones. I am doing this in the hope that they will get exhausted and go to sleep!"

27

Umar(ra) felt accountable, for he thought he had made arrangements to ensure that everyone had sufficient food. He left immediately and went to the *Bait ul Maal* (public treasury) and put the necessary provisions in a bag. Umar(ra) asked Aslam, his slave, to load the bag on his back.

28

Aslam offered to carry it for him. The Caliph carried the bag himself saying, "On the Day of Judgment, you will not be there to carry my burden for me."

One day, Firoz, a Persian nicknamed 'Abu Lulu' complained to Umar(ra) about the taxes he had to pay. When Umar(ra) told him, after twice enquiring into the matter, that the taxes were reasonable, he became very upset. The next day during the *Fajr Salaah* (Dawn prayers), he stabbed the Caliph six times and also wounded thirteen Muslims. He was uncontrollable. At last realizing that he could not escape, he stabbed himself to death. When Umar(ra) learned who the assassin was, he said, "Thank Allah he is not a Muslim!"

Umar(ra) prayed to Allah to pardon him, "If I had the earth full of gold, then I would give it in order to free myself of the Lord's

punishment before it descends on me." Hearing this, someone said to Umar(ra) that he had rendered great services to religion. He would surely have a great position with Allah. Umar(ra) replied, "If there is nothing for me or against me that will be enough."

Umar(ra) asked his son Abdullah to go to Aisha(ra) and beg her permission to be buried by the side of the Prophet. Aisha(ra) wept saying, "I wanted to reserve this spot for my own grave, but I prefer Umar(ra) to myself!" When Umar(ra) heard that she had consented, he sighed with relief, "It was the greatest wish of my life!"

Before he breathed his last, Umar(ra), like a true believer, said to his son, "Rub my cheek in the dust, Abdullah," and his son did as he was asked. Then with his head resting on the ground, Umar(ra) uttered these words: "Woe betide you, Umar(ra), and woe betide the one who gave birth to you if Allah does not forgive you." In death also he showed his humility. He had spent his life in the service of Allah and in establishing the ideals of Islam, but he felt as if he had done nothing.

Umar Farooq(ra), one of the greatest Caliph of Islam passed away on 1st of Muharram 644 C.E. after serving for ten years, six months and four days.

He did not nominate his successor but suggested that he who had the largest number of votes from among the six *Sahaba* (Companions) should be chosen. He advised his successor, whoever it was going to be, to fear Allah and protect the rights of the people (Muslims and non-Muslims) and always to keep his word.

His Caliphate, a great welfare state, was the highest point in early Islamic history. The old, the poor, the orphans and the disabled, both Muslims and non-Muslims alike were provided for from the *Bait ul Maal.* Everyone was equal and was treated with justice. Undoubtedly Umar Farooq(ra) was an exemplary human being and an ideal ruler.